The ditch is made, and our nails the spade, With pic-tures full, of wax and of wool: Their li-vers I stick with nee-dles quick; There lacks but the blood to make up the flood. Quick-ly, dame, then bring your part in!

Four Elizabethan Lyrics is a Sainsbury's Commission for Farnham Youth Choir,
Winner of the Sainsbury's Youth Choir of the Year 1992

FOUR ELIZABETHAN LYRICS
1. The owl is abroad

Words by Ben Jonson

RONALD CORP

OXFORD UPPER-VOICE MUSIC

General Editor Ronald Corp

W120

S.A.A. (with divisions) and piano

Four Elizabethan Lyrics

Ronald Corp

1. The owl is abroad
2. Golden slumbers
3. Elegy for himself
4. When daffodils begin to peer

CHORAL / VOCAL ARCHIVE SERVICE
Available from:
Banks Music Publications, The Granary,
Wath Court, Hovingham, York YO62 4NN
www.banksmusicpublications.co.uk
Photocopying copyright material is theft

Music Department
OXFORD UNIVERSITY PRESS
Oxford and New York

37

Spur,— spur u-pon lit - tle Mar - tin! Mer - ri - ly, mer - ri - ly, make him sail, A

41

worm in his mouth and a thorn in his tail,

45

SOPRANO *mf*

The owl is a-broad, the bat and the toad, And so is the cat - a-

ALTO *mf*

The owl is a-broad, the bat and the toad, And

*Optional bars in square brackets.

fire be - low, With a whip in your hand to

make him go! (O

now she's come! Let all be dumb.)

2. Golden slumbers

Words by Thomas Dekker

RONALD CORP

Sleep, pret-ty wan-tons, do not cry, And I will sing a

Sleep, pret-ty wan-tons, do not cry, And I will sing a

lul - la - by; Rock them, rock them, lul - la - by.

lul - la - by; Rock them, rock them, lul - la - by.

3. Elegy for himself

Words by Chidiock Tichbourne

RONALD CORP

Elegy for himself is also available for SATB chorus.

sun;   And   now I   live,   and now my life   is   done.

sun;   And   now I   live,   and now my life   is   done.

Coll' 8

SEMI-CHORUS*

Ah,   ah,   ah,   ah,

Ah,____   ah,____   ah,____   ah,____

MAIN CHORUS *mp*

My

*A few voices only, in three parts.

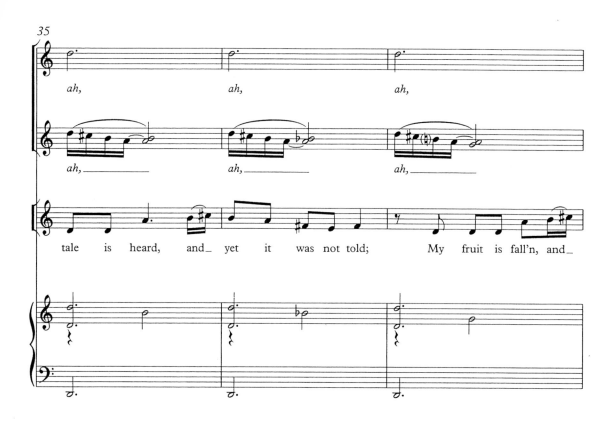

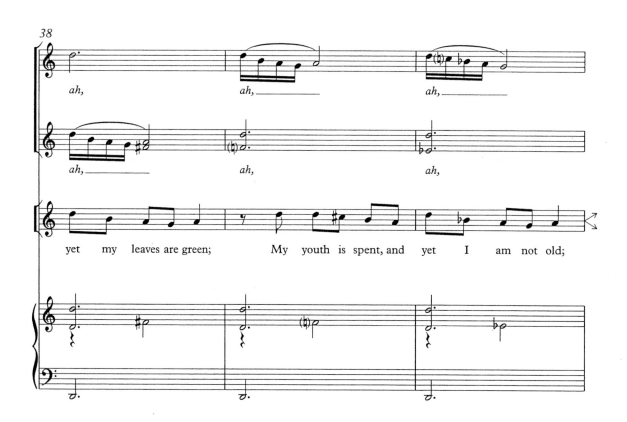

41

ah,　　　　　ah.　　　　　　　My thread is cut, and

ah,　　　　　ah.　　　　　　　My thread is cut, and

I saw the world, and yet　I　was not seen:　My thread is cut, and

I　saw the world, and yet　I　was not seen:　My thread is cut, and

Coll' 8

45　FULL

yet　it　is　not　spun;　And　now　I　live,　and　now my　life　is

FULL

yet　it　is　not　spun;　And　now　I　live,　and　now my　life　is

4. When daffodils begin to peer

Words by William Shakespeare

RONALD CORP

When daf-fo-dils be-gin to peer, With heigh, *(clap)* with heigh, the do-xy o-ver the dale, Why then comes in the sweet o' the year, For the red blood reigns in the win-ter's pale.

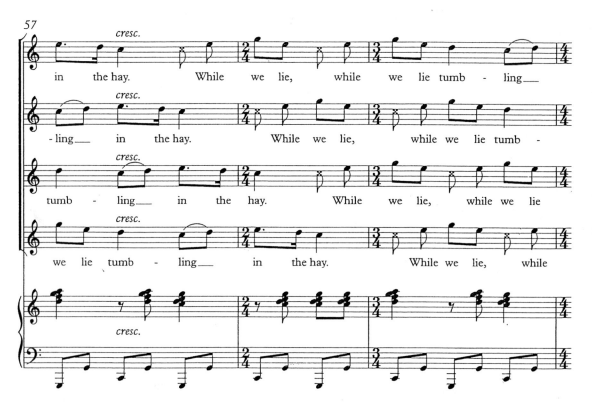

ISBN 0-19-342617-X

9 780193 426177

Music origination by Barnes Music Engraving Ltd., East Sussex
Printed in Great Britain by Halstan & Co. Ltd., Amersham, Bucks.